The Walk

Bones wanted a walk.
He got his lead.

Bones took the lead to his master.

Bones sat and sat.

GOOD EXERCISE!

age 2

age 14

Diana Bentley

Story illustrated by
Pet Gotohda

In this story

 Bones

 The master

 Wag

Tricky words

- wanted
- walk
- lead
- jumped

Introduce these tricky words and help the reader when they come across them later!

Story starter

Bones is a big dog. Wag is a small dog. Bones is a very good dog but Wag is always getting into trouble. One day, Bones wanted a walk so he got his lead.

The master sat up.

Bones gave his master
the lead.

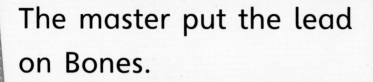

The master put the lead
on Bones.

"Good dog, Bones," said his master.

He gave Bones a bone.

Wag wanted a walk.
He got his lead.

Wag took the lead
to his master.

He jumped and jumped.

What do you think the master will say?

Wag jumped up on his master.

His master jumped up.

"Bad dog, Wag!"
said his master.

Quiz

Text Detective

- Why did the master say "Good dog, Bones"?
- Would you like Wag or Bones as your dog?

Word Detective

- **Phonic Focus:** Final phonemes

  Page 4: Find a word that ends with the phoneme 't'.
- Page 3: How many syllables (beats) are there in the word 'wanted'?
- Page 9: How many words are there in this sentence?

Super Speller

Read these words:

got   sat

Now try to spell them!

HA! HA! HA!

Q Why do dogs wag their tails?

A Because no one else will do it for them!

13

Find out about

- Giving pets exercise by taking them for walks

Tricky words

- exercise
- donkey
- walk
- master
- horse
- elephant

Introduce these tricky words and help the reader when they come across them later!

Text starter

A pet needs lots of exercise to keep it healthy. Some pets are easy to exercise, but some pets have to be taken for a walk every day.

Walkies!

A pet needs lots of exercise.

A donkey needs exercise.

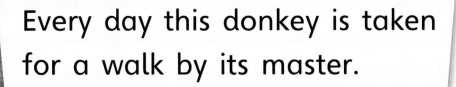

Every day this donkey is taken for a walk by its master.

It is good exercise.

A horse needs exercise.

Every day this horse is taken for a walk by its master.

It is good exercise.

An elephant needs exercise.

Every day this elephant is taken for a walk by its master.

It is good exercise.

A dog needs lots of exercise.

Quiz

Text Detective

- Which animals in the text need exercise?
- What would be the best thing about taking a dog for a walk?

Word Detective

- **Phonic Focus:** Final phonemes

  Page 19: Find a word that ends with the phoneme 'n'.
- Page 17: Find a word that means 'owner'.
- Page 17: Which word tells us about the exercise?

Super Speller

Read these words:

pet   for

Now try to spell them!

HA! HA! HA!

 Q What's the best country to take a horse for a walk?

A Horse-tralia.